BREAKAWAY MATHS

CD-ROM TEACHER'S GUIDE
(Second Edition)

GRANADA
Learning

ISBN 0-17-200001-7   Acorn version

ISBN 0-17-200002-5   PC version

NPN 9 8 7 6 5 4 3 2

CONTENTS

Acknowledgements

The publishers wish to acknowledge the contributions to the creation of this CD-ROM made by the following people

Authors
Peter Gash
Jenny Gash

Content co-ordinator
Joanna Daymond

Editor
Mairi Sutherland

Project Manager
Stephen Psallidas

Programmers
Denise Edwardson
Duncan Hoyle

Graphics
Simon Auchterlonie

Digitisation
Rauiri McGuinness
John Moore
Andrew Nesbitt

Children's voices
Sam Conway
Jessica Conway
Emily Hancock
Jonathan Mills

Additional Audio
Jayne Jermaine

Audio scripts
Emma Powell

Photography
Pam Campbell
Simon Auchterlonie

Thanks are also due to the following contributors:

Aritith Grey
Peter Hutchinson
Ken Milmore
Gerald Morris
Elaine Tarrant
Sheila Graber Animations Ltd
Wordley Productions
John Wright

The disc is set in Breakaway Park which is based entirely on Alton Towers theme park in Staffordshire, England. The publishers wish to extend their gratitude to the management of Alton Towers for the help received in producing this disc.

There are many attractions at Alton Towers but limitations on space has meant that only 12 are featured on the CD-ROM.

Visitors to the park should note that certain height restrictions apply to some of the rides featured on this disc. This may prevent some children accessing selected rides when they visit the park. The following height restrictions are currently in force:

Nemesis	1.4 metres
Congo River rapids	1.1 metres*
Runaway Mine Train	1.1 metres*
Enterprise	1.1 metres*
Wave Swinger	1.1 metres
Kiddies Kingdom	under 1.5 metres

* unless accompanied by an adult

Alton Towers is a division of the Tussauds Group Limited of Alton Towers, Staffordshire, England, ST10 4DB.

Welcome to the Breakaway Maths CD-ROM, designed by Peter and Jenny Gash and Granada Learning for Thomas Nelson and Sons Ltd. This fully interactive learning package is intended for use by pupils aged 7 to 12; in particular, those pupils who are having difficulty in making progress in mathematics.

The contents of the CD-ROM places mathematics in real life situations. These are all set inside the Breakaway Theme Park which is based on a real theme park, Alton Towers in Staffordshire, England. This location has been used to provide stimulating images and enjoyable activities. These are used within a strategy aimed at interesting and encouraging pupils while furthering their understanding. The disc can be used by individual pupils or by small groups.

Components of the pack

- CD-ROM
- User guide for teachers and parents

Overview

Pupils enter by typing in their personal password, or that of their group. They are then introduced to the park and complete a simple assess-ment exercise which sets the level of the questions they will meet later.

Once inside they are given a map which they must use to find their way around. Basic navigational skills are used in conjunction with the map to move between the 12 locations in Breakaway Park. As they move around the park, pupils are accompanied by four friends, Rupa, Lisa, Nicky and David, who provide help, guidance and encouragement. At each location they will encounter either an *activity area* or an *investigation area*.

Activity areas

There are six activity areas located at various *rides*. Each has two sets of questions with up to 10 questions in each set (see chart on page 27). The questions encountered will be set to the appropriate level for the pupil currently using the disc.

On arrival at an activity area, pupils are introduced visually to the ride and hear an audio commentary from their friends. Having completed a set of questions they will see the first half of a video of the ride. To see the rest they must complete the second set of questions. The video shows the ride as you would experience it if you were sitting on the ride itself.

On finishing the ride the friends re-appear to congratulate the pupils if they have done well or to provide encouragement if they have done less well. For more information on activity area questions please see pages 23 to 33.

Investigation areas

There are six investigation areas located at different *attractions*, (including the toyshop and restaurant). Each presents maths in a problem solving situation and each is set at three different levels. The *subjects* covered at the investigation areas are as follows:

Location:	Subject:
Skyride	Place value and digits in numbers
Explorer Restaurant	Food combinations
Courtyard	Triangular numbers
Old MacDonald's Farm	Squares
Kiddies Kingdom	3D shapes
Fabulous Toyshop	Coin combinations

Investigations involve work both on and off the CD-ROM. Pupils are asked an initial question which they must answer. Following instructions on screen they work through a sequence of questions. At an appropriate point they are prompted to continue their work off screen.

For more information on investigations see pages 35 to 52.

Audio

All the questions pupils encounter have audio instructions to help them. This facility can be controlled by the teacher or parent.

The map and navigation around the park

To move around Breakaway Park, pupils must use the on-screen map. This will enable them to find and select the various attractions as they would in a real life situation.

There is more information about the map on page 20.

Assessment

As pupils use the CD-ROM their progress is assessed and reported. Depending on their responses, the computer will move pupils on to a higher or lower level of question as they move around the park. They can leave the disc at any point. When they return, they will be automatically returned to the point at which they left, providing they enter their name on re-entry to the park.

For more on assessment please see page 54.

Teacher Options

Teachers and parents can use this facility to monitor pupils' progress as they use the disc over a period of time. The level of difficulty of the questions can be changed to suit individual needs and pupils can be directed to selected tasks as appropriate. Other options are available to help manage pupils' files.

See pages 56–59 for more details.

GETTING STARTED

System requirements

PC version

The recommended specification is as follows:

- 486 based IBM PC compatible computer (minimum 386)
- 4 megabytes memory
- SVGA Graphics (256 colour)
- MS-DOS 5.0 or above
- Microsoft Windows 3.1 or Windows 95
- CD-ROM drive (double speed)
- Mouse
- Sound card

Acorn version

- ARM 3 or above (minimum ARM 250)
- 4 megabytes memory
- SVGA (mode 28) graphics (640x480 256 colours)
- RISC-OS 3.1. or later
- CD-ROM drive (double speed)

Installation

PC version

1   Start Windows

2   Place the CD-ROM into your CD-ROM drive. Depending on the type of drive, you may need to put the disc into a caddy before proceeding.

3   Select 'Run...' from the File menu in Program Manager and type the following:

<drive>:\setup

where **<drive>** is the drive letter of your CD-ROM drive. For example, if your CD-ROM drive is set up as drive 'd' you would type: **d:\setup**

Press Enter or click OK. The Set-up program will now run.

4   Follow the instructions given in the Set-up program. This will install the software and create a program group in Program Manager.

Parts of the software can be installed on your hard disc. This makes it quicker to load than loading from the CD-ROM. The performance may also be improved.

5   Install Video for Windows (version 1.1) on to your system. If this has already been done you can skip this step. If you are not sure if you already have Video for Windows, you can reinstall it without any adverse effects i.e. select 'Run...' from the File menu in Program Manager and type the following:

<drive>:\video\setup

where **<drive>** is the drive letter of your CD-ROM drive. This will be the same as the drive letter you entered in Step 3. For example, if your CD-ROM drive is set up as drive 'd', you would type the following:

d:\video\setup

Press Enter or click on OK. The video Set-up program will now run.

6   Once the installation is complete, exit from Windows and reboot your system.

Acorn version

1 Load the CD-ROM into your CD-ROM drive. Depending upon the drive, you may need to put the disc into a caddy first.

2 When running the CD-ROM for the first time only, drag !MathsUser from the install directory to the directory where you wish to store your Breakaway Maths installation details. This directory must never be write protected.You must double click on your copy of !MathsUser at the start of any session using Breakaway Maths.

3 Click on the CD-ROM icon at the bottom of the screen to open a directory window. After a short pause you will see a window containing the Breakaway Maths CD-ROM icon.

4 Double click on this icon.

5 An introductory video will run at the end of which this same icon will appear on the Icon Bar at the bottom of your screen.

6 You are now ready to start the disc.

Running the CD-ROM

Once the installation procedures described above have been completed, you can use the CD-ROM by following the simple steps set out below:

PC version

1 Start Windows.

2 Place the **Breakaway Maths** CD-ROM into the CD-ROM drive.

3. Select the **Breakaway Maths** icon in Program Manager.

4. Double click on this icon to start the disc.

Acorn version

1 Once you have gone through the procedures outlined above all that is left is to single click on the icon in the Icon bar at the foot of the screen to start the disc.

All versions

1 Starting the disc will result in the opening menu being displayed on screen.

2 The first time you use the disc, move your cursor arrow over the words **Go to start**. A box will appear around them. Click on the left hand button of your mouse to move to the next screen.

3 Enter your name in the box containing the flashing vertical cursor. Remember that you are entering your personal password. You will need to use it again so it should be spelt with care.

4 Click on **OK** to move into the disc.

5 If you are re-entering the disc, at the opening menu screen move your cursor arrow over the words **Go back to the park**. A box will appear around them. Click on the left hand button of your mouse to move to the next screen.

Helpline

If you have any problems running the Breakaway Maths CD-ROM, please phone the Granada Learning Customer Services Helpline on 0161 827 2778. Hardware problems should be referred to the supplier.

Guide to the icons

As you use this CD-ROM you will encounter buttons (icons) that will enable you to get the most out of the disc. In each case, use the mouse to place the cursor over the required buttons. Click on the left mouse button to activate the facility or tool.

Buttons used on the map screen

Click on... to...

 move in the direction of the arrow you have selected

 move around the park (you cannot move and look at the same time)

 look at pathways and views around the park (to change between LOOK and MOVE, click on the smaller word)

 obtain help with the current screen

 go to the menu screen

Buttons used in the investigations

Click on... to...

 obtain help with the current screen

 go to the menu screen

 see the progress being made by a pupil

 hear again what Rupa, Lisa, Nicky and David said

 go back to the map

 move to the next screen

 continue the investigation by selecting either YES or NO

 hear the question

 end this question

 move back to see some real-life examples

 move forward to see some more real-life examples

Buttons used in the activities

Click on... to see...

 obtain help with the current screen

 go to the menu screen

 see the progress being made by a pupil

 move to the next screen

 move back to the previous screen

Video controls

 play video

 pause video

 fast forward

 rewind video

 return to start of video

Click on these icons...for questions about...

 Number and algebra (1) – number and place value

 Number and algebra (2) – number and pattern

 Number and algebra (3) – money and problem solving

 Shape and space (1) – shape, position and movement

 Shape and space (2) – measurement including time

 Handling data

Buttons used in the Teachers Options

Click on... to...

 cancels changes made to the level of questions by the teacher and restores the original level set by the computer

 obtain help with the current screen

 go to the menu screen

 turn sound on and off (toggle)

 display the progress charts of the name highlighted in the list

Subject Areas show the progress chart for the 6 subject areas

Problem - Solving Areas show the progress chart for the 6 problem-solving areas (to move between histograms click on the title box)

NA1 / 1 display educational information relevant to the subject or problem-solving area

 move back to the previous screen

Guided tour

Sample routes

To familiarise yourself with the features and working of this program you may find it useful to run through the following routines. All selections are made by moving the mouse to place the arrow on your choice and clicking the left hand button.

1. Getting started the first time you use the CD-ROM

Action..	to see...
At the opening screen move your cursor over '**Go to start**' and click.	A screen requesting that you type in your name or that of your group. This is your personal password.
Type in your name or your group name. This is now your password. Write this name down and keep it safe. Now click on the **OK** button.	The four children, Nicky, David, Rupa and Lisa who will be going round the park with you will introduce themselves.
Click on the **continue** button when it appears at the bottom of the screen theme park.	A video will play showing the monorail that takes visitors into the theme park. You can use the video controls under the screen to rewind, fast-forward, stop and play the video.
Click on the **continue** button at the bottom of the screen	The ticket kiosk at the entrance to the park. Listen to the audio.
Click on the **continue** button at the bottom of the screen.	This is the first series of questions. Answering these questions is your entry ticket into the park. These questions are only presented on your first visit to the park.
Read the questions at the top of each screen.	
Click on the loudspeaker button.	You will hear the question.
Answer the questions by clicking on the correct answer or by clicking and dragging answers to the correct box.	Go to the next question by a) clicking on **continue** and/or b) clicking on the open door and flashing arrow in the top right of the screen.

When you have finished the final question the children on the CD-ROM will tell you.

Click on the **continue** button when it appears	The video introduction to the park. Try the video controls.
Click on the **continue** button when it appears at the end of the audio.	The map of Breakaway Park

2. Finding your way around the park

Action..	to see...
Having entered the park and answered the initial set of questions you will arrive at a map of Breakaway Park.	Your personal password will appear in a box in the bottom left-hand corner of the screen. Your position in the park is marked by the **red and white box** on the map
Click on the **MOVE/LOOK** button	The four children appear and the arrow buttons are clearly visible at the foot of the screen. You have changed to **LOOK mode** and you can now take a look around you.
Click on each **arrow button** in turn.	You will see a view of the actual park in the direction of the arrow.
When you are ready to move along a path, click on the **MOVE/LOOK** button.	You have returned to the map of Breakaway park and you are in **MOVE mode**.
Click on the **left arrow**.	The position marker moves to the left. An audio message informs you that **'We are one step away from the Skyride'**
Click on the **downward pointing** arrow	You have arrived at the Skyride title screen.

Return to the map by clicking on the Map button or progress through the investigation by following the text/audio instructions on screen.

3. Re-entering the park

If you have used the disc before, the introductory screens and assessment questions will be by-passed and you return to the point on the disc at which you made your last exit.

Action..	to see...
At the opening screen, move your cursor over **Go back to the park** and click.	A list of the current users of the CD-ROM
Find your personal password on the list, place the cursor over it and click or type in your name/password.	Your personal password will appear in the box.
Click on the **OK** button.	You will be taken directly to the point at which you left off when last you used the disc.

IN THE CLASSROOM

Breakaway Maths CD-ROM has been specially devised and written for children who have problems with learning mathematics. It provides content from Key Stage 1 and Key Stage 2 (England and Wales) for 7 to 11 year olds who are struggling with maths or have some special need which means they require more materials, more time or a longer learning curve. The content also relates to Levels A and B of the Mathematics 5 – 14 Guidelines in Scotland and Levels 1 to 3 of the Northern Ireland Curriculum Mathematics order (see chart on page 27 for correlation).

All of the writing has been informed by the best practices in mathematics education from the Cockroft Report (HMSO 1982) through the development of the National Curriculum to the Dearing Report and revisions of 1995.

In addition to this CD-ROM and Teachers Guide, the Breakaway Maths scheme offers sets of textbooks, workbooks, copymasters and Teacher's Resource Books. The CD-ROM and the book series have been designed and written to work independently and each provides extensive maths resources in its own right. Together they provide a massive bank of materials for children with special needs in mathematics.

Maths on a CD-ROM?

It is not intended that this CD-ROM should replace any of the key aspects of learning mathematics. Children will always need to handle and make shapes, manipulate apparatus, devise their own charts, ways of working and patterns. Neither is a theme park the only environment rich in mathematical content. The disc can, however, be used in many ways:

- It can be at the core of a group's maths programme, but with the children moving away from it regularly to look at more examples of the maths they are covering.

- It can be used to introduce an aspect of mathematics, like 2D shapes, which is then followed up using different materials and activities.

- It can be used to reinforce or enrich a skill or concept developed from other sources.

- It can be the starting point (or provide another example of) an investigation. In fact, the investigations are developed by sending children away from the computer to collect more data (see pages 36 to 37).

Teachers can use the Teacher Options (pages 56 to 59) to exploit any of the above methods of working.

Organising time on the computer

Unless a classroom is blessed with many computers, children will have to share computer time. A session of about 20 to 30 minutes is ideal for children to use the Breakaway Maths CD-ROM on a daily basis. As there are only between 4 and 5 hours available per day, this limits the number of individuals who could use it during one day. It is ideal therefore to organise children into pairs or small groups.

Children working in pairs or groups experience more than just the mathematics. They learn to co-operate, listen to others, weigh up options, discuss decisions and review results. They may also wish to keep written notes of what they are doing (especially in the investigations) and take turns to use the keyboard or mouse. When they move away from the computer they can help each other with apparatus and model making.

Before children begin their adventure at Breakaway Park they need to log on with their group name. This is their personal password, and every time they use it they return to exactly the place they left at the end of the last session. To cover several groups it is a good idea to choose uncommon names, e.g. eagles, falcons, kestrels, hawks. Teachers also need to use the children's personal password to access progress reports once in the Teacher Options (see page 56).

A good way to ensure each group has a 'fair' amount of time is to use a kitchen timer set at 20 or 30 minutes. When the group logs on they start the timer. When it rings or bleeps it is time for the next group to begin.

There may be times when a teacher wishes an individual to use an aspect of the CD-ROM as part of an assessment. For example a child can be 'set' a series of questions on a particular aspect of mathematics, and on completion the teacher can use the Teacher Options to review the percentage success.

Interacting: the activity area questions

The CD-ROM makes little use of the keyboard. Children generally use a mouse or tracker ball to make their intentions known to the computer. They also use this to look at the map, move around the park, look at viewpoints and ask for audio help. Symbols showing the options open to them appear on each screen. Children move to the symbol and 'click' on it. If an option is not available then the symbol is omitted. For example, there is no audio at a viewpoint, just a picture; therefore the audio symbol does not appear.

More importantly children move to and 'click' on answers to questions. To maintain variety and interest, different types of screen question are used, requiring children to perform different actions to answer. All types of question include a statement/question at the top of the screen (with audio), and most include a picture (drawing or photo) as the main resource in the centre of the screen.

True or false?

There is a picture in the centre of the screen, relating to the statement or question. Children choose between two answers at the bottom of the screen and click on the one they think is correct.

Click on the correct label

The statement/question relates to a picture with several labels attached to it. Children click on one or more correct labels.

Choose the correct label

The statement/question relates to a picture which has one or more blank labels. At the bottom of the screen there are several labels to choose from. Children pick up and drag the labels to the appropriate blank spaces.

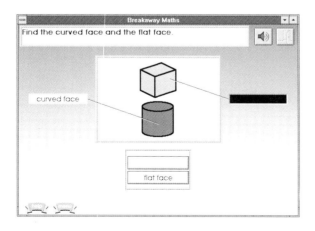

Multiple choice

There is a main picture relating to the statement/question, and several possible answers below. Children click on the correct answer.

Sorting

Instead of one main picture relating to the statement/question, there are several mixed up items and two or three (empty) labelled columns. Children sort the items by picking up and dragging each item into the appropriate column.

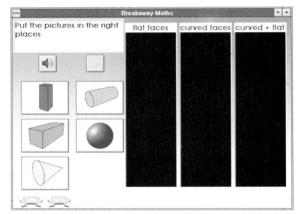

Matching

The statement/question relates to two rows (or columns) of matchable items, with a blank row in between. The items in one row are fixed, but the items in the other row are movable. Children pick each movable item up and drag it to the appropriate position in the blank row, beneath the matching item.

After each question there is a brief response to the child's answer. Responses have been designed to reflect children's success without being negative. If they have answered correctly they are congratulated. If they are wrong the response encourages them to carry on and try again. The computer keeps track of all responses. These can be checked through the Teacher Options (see page 56).

The investigations use the same routines and screens as listed here. The structure and requirements of the investigations are described in detail on pages 35 to 52.

Initial assessment

After the disc has been opened up on screen, children see the titles credits and main menu. They should select 'Go to start'. They will then be asked to type in their own name or group name, which will be stored on the hard disc. They must use this name every time they return to the park. The hard disc will also store all the information about where they have been, the level they are on, and how well they are doing.

Once the correct name has been entered, the children meet the screen characters who guide them around Breakaway Park. This is the only time the children visit here. In future sessions they will automatically return to where they finished in the park the last time. At the entrance kiosk they are asked some simple mathematical questions. The computer uses these to assign a starting level for their trip

around the park. The children are not told this level, but teachers can access it through the Teacher Options (see page 56).

This initial assessment automatically defaults to the lowest level appropriate. Children with difficulties will start at the beginning of Level 1. Children who are more successful will begin at Level 2. This is to allow the children access to questions they can cope with at this early stage. As children work their way around the park the computer will continually modify the levels depending on their successes and failures. The aim is to provide appropriate questions right across the maths curriculum. For example, some children may be coping with shape and space very well, but still have problems with handling data. Shape questions will be set at a higher level than those for handling data.

Full records are kept under the pupil's own or group name on the hard disc. Teacher Options allow teachers to look at these at any time, even when the user is working on the problems.

Moving around the map

The map of Breakaway Park is a simplified representation of parts of Alton Towers. All of the features are in the correct places. The limits of space dictated that we use just six rides and six attractions. However, there is plenty of excitement and maths to experience.

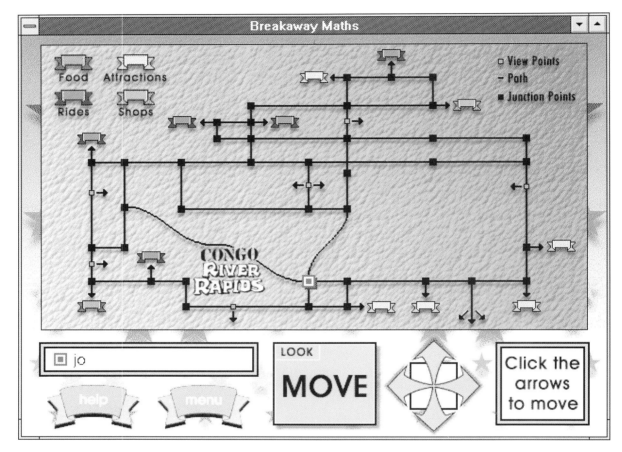

Children should explore the map first. Each flag on the map represents either a ride (blue flag), an attraction (yellow flag) or shop (green flag) or eating place (red flag). To find out what is at each flag simply click on it: the name of the ride or attraction will appear. The lines and attractions are linked by a network of black lines representing paths, and along the paths there are small black squares (junction points) and some blue spots, representing viewpoints. (Viewpoints have been included to let children see more of the park. They are intended to improve the sense of 'being there' and to enhance the geography.)

Two different modes are available on the screen map: Move and Look (selected by clicking the MOVE/LOOK button). In Move mode pupils can travel around the map, by clicking on the direction arrows at the foot of the screen. Children can only move along the paths shown, from junction to junction with each move. If a direction is not available at a particular junction then the relevant arrow will not appear on screen. When the children are at the closest junction to an attraction or ride they receive audio hints from the four screen characters on how to reach it.

Look mode can be used at any junction point on the map (not just the viewpoints). When Look mode is selected, children can click on the arrows to see a photograph of what they would see in the real park, in the direction they have chosen.

Rides

Six rides are used to present sets of questions on the following areas of the maths curriculum:

- Number
- Shape, Space and Measures
- Handling Data

The six rides are:

Nemesis,

Enterprise,

Wave Swinger,

Runaway Mine Train,

Congo River Rapids,

Toyland Tours.

Each ride has two sets of questions with up to 10 questions in each set. Each set covers a different aspect of the mathematics curriculum. For example, on Nemesis there are ten questions on Number and ten questions on Shape, Space and Measures (see chart on page 27). Wherever possible the questions use some aspect of the ride as the context.

After children have completed the first set of questions they can go on the first half of the ride. They see this as a real-time video. They can do this as many times as they like. They can even use the video control buttons to do it in reverse, slow motion or pause it anywhere they want. To see the complete ride they will need to do the second set of questions. Once they have done these then they can use the ride as many times as they like, forwards, backwards and in slow motion until they decide to go elsewhere. If they return to the ride and have moved up or down a stage, they must do the questions again to see the video. If they have stayed at the same stage, clicking on that subject gives a prompt suggesting they try a different ride (where the same subject is covered), but they can do the original questions again if they wish.

There are more details about each ride and the areas of the maths curriculum associated with them on pages 23 to 33.

Attractions

The attractions are used as starting points for problem solving and investigations. At some point during the activity children will be asked to leave the computer and carry on with their investigation using copymasters, apparatus, or pencils and paper. They can then return and show what they have found out.

The problems/investigations fall under the following headings

▨ Place value and digits in numbers

▨ Food combinations

▨ Triangular numbers

▨ Squares

▨ 3D shapes

▨ Coin combinations

Children find themselves, with the four screen characters, in a shop, snack bar or attraction. The characters introduce the initial problem, and children are taken through one or two examples. The computer shows them the materials they will need, and suggests how to record their results. After the introduction they are sent away to continue with the problem or investigation. When they have gathered more data they can return and input it, with the computer showing their results on screen. When all of the results are in, they are congratulated and shown some further pictorial examples of where the problem or investigation occurs in real life. They are then free to leave and return to the map.

Children can return to the investigations as often as they like. If they are successful, then the investigation is extended to include more or harder examples, and elements of looking for patterns or making predictions.

The six investigations can be found at:

▨ Skyride

▨ Explorer Restaurant

▨ Courtyard,

▨ Old MacDonald's Farm,

▨ Kiddies Kingdom

▨ Fabulous Toyshop

There are more detailed descriptions of the investigations, and suggestions as to the kinds of materials children will need, on pages 39 to 52.

At any time, during a ride or an attraction, children can leave the park by clicking on Menu. All of their work and progress will be recorded by the computer before the program ends. When they return, they will begin at the exact place where they quit last time.

SCOPE & SEQUENCE:
ACTIVITY AREA QUESTIONS
(RIDES)

USING AND APPLYING MATHEMATICS

GENERAL STRUCTURE

NEMESIS

ENTERPRISE

WAVE SWINGER

RUNAWAY MINE TRAIN

CONGO RIVER RAPIDS

TOYLAND TOURS

Using and Applying Mathematics

It is not possible for any published scheme of work to cover Using and Applying Mathematics/Processes/Problem solving in complete detail. Many aspects can only be addressed in the classroom by the teacher. However, the Breakaway Maths CD-ROM does give opportunities for children to experience many aspects of this very important area.

Using and Applying Mathematics 1

The Breakaway Maths CD-ROM presents the majority of problems in the context of real-life situations. If children work in pairs or groups they will discuss and explain their thinking to each other as they decide how to reach a solution.

Using and Applying Mathematics 2

Screens on the CD-ROM present problems in a variety of ways. Children will have to select the mathematics they are going to use to find an answer. Once again, if they work together they will monitor and criticise each other's decisions and thinking.

Using and Applying Mathematics 3

The CD-ROM provides an ideal medium for presenting mathematical problems using a variety of language, pictures, words, audio and symbols. Working together, children will begin to use mathematical terms and translate for each other as a natural part of using the program.

Using and Applying Mathematics 4

The images on the CD-ROM will encourage children to tease the mathematics out of situations. When navigating around the park they will need to make predictions, often based on previous experiences. The attractions (investigations) provide many opportunities for children to search for and identify patterns. They will ask questions and be able to test them as well as being encouraged to make simple generalisations and projections.

General structure

On the CD-ROM, the mathematics curriculum has been divided into the following subject areas:

Number and algebra 1 (NA1)

Number and algebra 2 (NA2)

Number and algebra 3 (NA3)

Shape and space 1 (SS1)

Shape and space 2 (SS2)

Handling Data (HD)

Within the National Curriculum, the subject areas of Breakaway Maths CD-ROM align with all of the Key Stage 1 Programme of Study, and some of the early Key Stage 2 Programme of Study as follows:

NA1 correlates with Number 2a, b and c

NA2 correlates with Number 3a, b, c, d and e

NA3 correlates with Number 4a, b, c, and d

SS1 correlates with Shape, Space and Measures 2a, b and c and Shape, Space and Measures 3a and b

SS2 correlates with Shape, Space and Measures 4a and b

HD correlates with Number 5a and b.

Each subject area is divided into 12 stages covering the equivalent of National Curriculum Levels 1, 2 and 3:

stages 1 to 4 cover Level 1,

stages 5 to 8 cover Level 2,

stages 9 to 12 cover Level 3.

Within the Northern Ireland Curriculum the subject areas of Breakaway Maths CD-ROM align with the attainment targets as follows: NA1, NA2 and NA3 correlate with Number and Algebra; SS1 and SS2 correlate with Shape and Space, and Measures; HD correlates with Handling Data.

For classes following the 5–14 Guidelines in Scotland: NA1, NA2 and NA3 support work in Number, Money and Measurement; SS1 and SS2 support Shape, Position and Movement and HD supports work in Information Handling.

Stage 1 represents introductory work at Level 1 while stage 4 represents the skills, knowledge and concepts that are achieved at the end of this Level. Stage 5 then introduces work at Level 2 and so on through to stage 12 which represents work at the end of Level 3.

To give an example of how this works on the disc:

Number 2abc is concerned with 'Developing an understanding of place value'.

At stage 1 the work is on counting, ordering and recognising the numbers up to 3.

Chart 1 – How the 12 stages correlate to the UK curricula

	Stages		
Curriculum	1 2 3 4	5 6 7 8	9 10 11 12
National Curriculum	Level 1	Level 2	Level 3
Northern Ireland	Level 1	Level 2	Level 3
Scotland	Level A	Level A/B	Level B

By stage 4 children will be counting, ordering and recognising the numbers up to 10.

Stage 6 is part of Level 2, and children will be counting, ordering and recognising the numbers up to 50 with special emphasis on tens and ones and place value.

By stage 8 at Level 2 children will progress to 100, round to the nearest 10 on a number line and begin to explore simple fractions of shapes and numbers.

At Level 3 stages 9 to 12, children will continue by counting, ordering and recognising numbers to 10 000 and recognise the place value of the digits. They will also round numbers to the nearest 10 and 100. The work on fractions extends to include thirds, fifths and tenths and they will begin to use simple decimals with money. They will also see some negative numbers in the context of thermometers and on number lines.

The aim of this structure is to give children a slow and steady progression towards each Attainment Target, with plenty of revisiting of topics. However, the structure of the program allows those who are successful to move more rapidly through the work they are happy with.

As a simple guide, Chart 2 shows the main subject areas covered by each ride.

P O S / Ride	Number 2	Number 3	Number 4	Number 5	Shape, Space & Measures 2	Shape, Space & Measures 3	Shape, Space & Measures 4
Nemesis		●			●	●	
Enterprise			●	●			
Wave Swinger	●						●
Runaway Mine Train		●			●	●	
Congo River Rapids	●		●				
Toyland Tours				●			●
Northern Ireland	N and A	N and A	N and A	D	M and S	M and S	M and S
Scotland	Number, Money and Measurement			Information Handling	Shape, Position and Movement		

Chart 2 – How the Programmes of Study are organised between rides.

This chart is based on the National Curriculum for England and Wales (1995).
The headings below the chart provide approximate correlations for:
The Northern Ireland Curriculum (Levels 1 to 3) and
Mathematics 5 – 14 in Scotland (Levels A and B).

Nemesis is a fast and furious ride. Passengers are suspended in safety harnesses so that their legs swing free. The ride travels at 20 to 30 metres per second and executes loops and rolls as well as rising and plunging. The average duration of the ride is about 1 minute 20 seconds. The structure shows lots of examples of cylinders and triangles used for strength and bracing.

When children visit Nemesis they will experience problems drawn from the following Programme of Study sections: Number 3abcd, Shape, Space and Measures 2abc and Shape, Space and Measures 3ab.

Number 3a	Repeating patterns of colour and number
Number 3b	Patterns of multiples of 2, 3, 4 and 5 Missing numbers in lines and arrays Odd and even numbers
Number 3c	Addition and subtraction facts (to 20) Addition and subtraction in pictorial form (to 1000) Multiplication and division facts (2x, 3x, 4x, 5x and 10x) Division with remainders (2x, 3x, 4x and 5x tables)
Number 3d	Choosing when to add or subtract Finding missing numbers and functions in simple additions and subtractions (<20) Finding half or quarter of an amount by partitioning and sharing
Shape, Space and Measures 2a	Continuing and finding the next shape in a pattern
Shape, Space and Measures 2b	Recognising and naming 3D shapes Labelling surfaces 'flat' or 'curved' Sorting 3D shapes according to criteria Recognising and naming 2D shapes Labelling straight and curved edges and corners Sorting 2D shapes according to criteria
Shape, Space and Measures 2c	Recognising the geometrical features of 3D and 2D shapes Recognising simple reflective symmetry
Shape, Space and Measures 3a	Describing positions (high, low, above, etc.) Simple 10x10 letter and number co-ordinates Compass points (N, S, E, W) Movements (left, right, up, down) Following instructions Finding rotated shapes
Shape, Space and Measures 3b	Recognising right angles Right-angled turns

ENTERPRISE

Enterprise is a high-speed roundabout, with the added interest of lifting to a near vertical position. Riders sit in enclosed gondolas in twos. This may be useful when counting in twos. The ride may also be useful for looking at rotation, circular movements and circles.

When children visit Enterprise they will experience problems drawn from the following Programme of Study sections: Number 3e; Number 4abc; and Number 5ab (Handling Data).

Please note that the calculator which is shown on screen does not function. It is there to provide children with a picture clue. Therefore they will need access to a classroom calculator to help them with the problems.

Number 3e	Using a calculator and interpreting the display
Number 4a	Addition and subtraction problems to 10
	Addition and subtraction problems to 100
	Addition and subtraction problems with exchange of tens
	Addition and subtraction problems using coins to 10p, leading to amounts up to £20
	Adding bills and giving change
	Equivalence of coins
	Money and decimal notation
Number 4b	Using multiplication and division
	Using a calculator to multiply and divide
	Multiplication and division of money
	Using the decimal point on the calculator
Number 4c	Choosing between addition and subtraction to solve a problem
	Using a calculator and interpreting the display
Number 5a	Sorting by colour, shape and size
	Using a Carroll diagram to sort
	Using a Venn diagram to sort
	Sorting into columns
Number 5b	Mapping one to one and one to many
	Tallying to collect data
	Making a block chart
	Interpreting tallies, block charts, Venn and Carroll diagrams
	Reading charts with scales
	Interpreting price lists

WAVE SWINGER

The Wave Swinger is a roundabout where the passengers are suspended in swings from chains. As well as turning around, the ride also tilts to give the impression of diving and swooping. There are many patterns on the ride itself, and arrangements of light bulbs up and down the structure. Each chair is supported by four chains, which may help when looking at groups of four.

When children visit Wave Swinger they will experience problems drawn from the following Programme of Study sections: Number 2abc; and Shape, Space and Measures 4ab.

Number 2a	Counting to 10 and beyond using objects and photographs
	Matching pictures and words to a number up to 1000
Number 2b	Reading writing and ordering numbers to 10 000
	Ordering highest to lowest, lowest to highest, fewest to most
	Numbers which come before or after
	Pictorial forms of place value, from tens and ones to thousands, hundreds, tens and ones
	Rounding numbers to 10 and 100
	Using number lines
Number 2c	Simple halves and quarters
	Relationship of fractions to a whole one
	Introduction of thirds, fifths and tenths
	Decimals as price tags (to £20)
	Negative numbers using thermometers and number lines
Shape, Space and Measures 4a	Language of measurement: long, short, wide, and narrow, etc.
	Estimating length with non-standard measures
	Introducing metres, half-metres and centimetres
	Language of weight: heavy, light, weighs more
	Introducing kilograms, half-kilograms and grams
	Adding weights
	Language of capacity: full, empty, half-full
	Introducing litres, half-litres and millilitres
	Adding capacities
	Estimating in standard units of length, weight and capacity
	Using metric abbreviations
	Conservation of area
	Areas using squares
	Times of day and days of the week
	Analogue and digital times
	Times including o'clock, half-past, quarter past/to, 5 minute and 1 minute intervals, a.m. and p.m.
Shape, Space and Measures 4b	Choosing a measuring instrument for a task
	Reading scales on rulers, weighing apparatus and measuring cylinders
	Reading a calendar
	Reading times and durations on a TV guide

RUNAWAY MINE TRAIN

The Runaway Mine Train is a roller coaster ride. Apart from the engine, each coach seats four people. This may be useful when looking at groups of 4 and the 4 times table. The ride is surrounded with structures to represent an old North American mine. There are lots of irregular 2D shapes made from poles. There are also lots of wonderful gears and pulleys. The roof structures are good examples of cones and pyramids.

When children visit The Runaway Mine Train they will experience problems drawn from the following Programme of Study sections: Number 3abcd; Shape, Space and Measures 2abc; and Shape, Space and Measures 3ab.

Number 3a	Repeating patterns of colour and number
Number 3b	Patterns of multiples of 2, 3, 4 and 5
	Missing numbers in lines and arrays
	Odd and even numbers
Number 3c	Addition and subtraction facts (to 20)
	Addition and subtraction in pictorial form (to 1000)
	Multiplication and division facts (2x, 3x, 4x, 5x and 10x)
	Division with remainders (2x, 3x, 4x and 5x tables)
Number 3d	Choosing when to add or subtract
	Finding missing numbers and functions in simple additions and subtractions (<20)
	Finding half or quarter of an amount by partitioning and sharing
Shape, Space and Measures 2a	Continuing and finding the next shape in a pattern
Shape, Space and Measures 2b	Recognising and naming 3D shapes
	Labelling surfaces 'flat' or 'curved'
	Sorting 3D shapes according to criteria
	Recognising and naming 2D shapes
	Labelling straight and curved edges and corners
	Sorting 2D shapes according to criteria
Shape, Space and Measures 2c	Recognising the geometrical features of 3D and 2D shapes
	Recognising simple reflective symmetry
Shape, Space and Measures 3a	Describing positions (high, low, above, etc.)
	Simple 10x10 letter and number co-ordinates
	Compass points (N, S, E, W)
	Movements (left, right, up, down)
	Following instructions
	Finding rotated shapes
Shape, Space and Measures 3b	Recognising right angles
	Right-angled turns

This is a wild, wet ride. The circular rubber boats contain up to six people, and this may provide opportunities to look at additions and subtractions. The boats themselves have a 2-digit number on the side.

When children visit Congo River Rapids they will experience problems drawn from the following Programme of Study sections: Number 2abc; and Number 4abc.

Please note that the calculator which is shown on screen does not function. It is there to provide children with a picture clue. Therefore they will need access to a classroom calculator to help them with the problems.

Number 2a	Counting to 10 and beyond using objects and photographs
	Matching pictures and words to a number up to 1000
Number 2b	Reading, writing and ordering numbers to 10 000
	Ordering highest to lowest, lowest to highest, fewest to most
	Numbers which come before or after
	Pictorial forms of place value, from tens and ones to thousands, hundreds, tens and ones
	Rounding numbers to 10 and 100
	Using number lines
Number 2c	Simple halves and quarters
	Relationship of fractions to a whole one
	Introduction of thirds, fifths and tenths
	Decimals as price tags (to £20)
	Negative numbers using thermometers and number lines
Number 4a	Addition and subtraction problems to 10
	Addition and subtraction problems to 100
	Addition and subtraction problems with exchange of tens
	Addition and subtraction problems using coins to 10p, leading to amounts up to £20
	Adding bills and giving change
	Equivalence of coins
	Money and decimal notation
Number 4b	Using multiplication and division
	Using a calculator to multiply and divide
	Multiplication and division of money
	Using the decimal point on the calculator
Number 4c	Choosing between addition and subtraction to solve a problem
	Using a calculator and interpreting the display

TOYLAND TOURS

Toyland Tours is one of the gentler rides. It is a slow canal boat ride through a toy, cake and sweet factory. There are many opportunities to look at patterns, shapes and colours during the video. There are also several examples of scales and graphs. It may be possible for children to use the sequence for tallying some of the objects they see.

When children visit Toyland Tours they will experience problems drawn from the following Programme of Study sections: Number 5ab (Handling Data); and Shape, Space and Measures 4ab.

Number 5a	Sorting by colour, shape and size
	Using a Carroll diagram to sort
	Using a Venn diagram to sort
	Sorting into columns
Number 5b	Mapping one to one and one to many
	Tallying to collect data
	Making a block chart
	Interpreting tallies, block charts, Venn and Carroll diagrams
	Reading charts with scales
	Interpreting price lists
Shape, Space and Measures 4a	Language of measurement: long, short, wide, and narrow, etc.
	Estimating length with non-standard measures
	Introducing metres, half-metres and centimetres
	Language of weight: heavy, light, weighs more
	Introducing kilograms, half-kilograms and grams
	Adding weights
	Language of capacity: full, empty, half-full
	Introducing litres, half-litres and millilitres
	Adding capacities
	Estimating in standard units of length, weight and capacity
	Using metric abbreviations
	Conservation of area
	Areas using squares
	Times of day and days of the week
	Analogue and digital times
	Times including o'clock, half-past, quarter past/to, 5 minute and 1 minute intervals, a.m. and p.m.
Shape, Space and Measures 4b	Choosing a measuring instrument for a task
	Reading scales on rulers, weighing apparatus and measuring cylinders
	Reading a calendar
	Reading times and durations on a TV guide

All of the rides can be used by teachers to set up sets of assessment questions at whichever level they wish. Also, a specific set of maths content can be assessed separately. This may be useful when developing Individual Education Plans for children. See 'Set the level of questions' on page 58.

SCOPE & SEQUENCE:
INVESTIGATIONS
(ATTRACTIONS)

USING AND APPLYING MATHEMATICS

GENERAL STRUCTURE

ASSESSING THE INVESTIGATIONS ON THE COMPUTER

SKYRIDE

EXPLORER RESTAURANT

COURTYARD

OLD MACDONALD'S FARM

KIDDIES KINGDOM

FABULOUS TOYSHOP

Using and Applying Mathematics

Investigations on the CD-ROM provide many opportunities to address the Using and Applying Mathematics/ Problem Solving/Processes strands in the Curriculum. However, some aspects will still need to be teased out in the classroom by the teacher.

Using and Applying Mathematics 1

The investigations use real-life situations as starting points. Children working in pairs or groups will discuss and explain their thinking to each other as they decide how they are going to reach a solution. Teachers will need to ask children to explain their progress, thinking and reasoning, using questions such as:

'What are you going to (could you) try next?'

'Show me how you found these results.'

'How does this pattern work?'

Using and Applying Mathematics 2

Starting points for the investigations on the CD-ROM need to be structured for the computer to be able to present and monitor them. There are also suggestions as to the materials children could use. However, teachers should encourage children to explore alternative methods of working, and ask them to select the materials which suit their needs. Some children will have favourite apparatus, and may be able to suggest new ways to use it.

Initially children find it difficult to organise their work. They may try many random examples and fail to perceive any pattern. Appropriate teacher intervention is important. This is best done through discussing and offering suggestions for ways of approaching work. Often children working in this environment will gradually contribute their own ideas quite readily.

Using and Applying Mathematics 3

The CD-ROM provides an ideal medium for presenting mathematical problems in a variety of ways, using pictures, words, audio and symbols. Working together, children will begin to use mathematical terms and translate for each other as a natural part of using the program.

When children are sent away from the screen to pursue the investigation, teachers should encourage them to continue to use the mathematical language they are developing as a natural way of speaking. They should also be free to try different methods of presenting their work.

Using and Applying Mathematics 4

The images on screen will encourage children to tease the mathematics out of situations. Investigating will naturally lead them to try to make predictions based on what they have encountered so far. Investigations also provide many opportunities for children to search for and identify patterns. They will ask questions and be able to test these on the computer, as well as being encouraged to make simple generalisations and projections. The final screens will suggest other situations in which they may find similar phenomena and patterns.

General structure

There are six attractions. Each one is the starting point for an investigation. Investigations are organised into three levels. For children who are assessed as still working towards Level 1 the investigations are kept simple and involve recognising simple patterns, collecting a limited amount of data and entering it into the computer. Level 2 extends the same investigation to include more examples and perhaps different criteria. Level 3 continues this and includes some aspect of recognising and describing a pattern. Sometimes at Level 3 children are asked to predict or make a simple generalisation.

At all levels children are initially shown a problem or a situation. They then work through one or two examples on screen. They are then asked to go away and continue to explore the problem. The equipment they need is also shown, and some suggestions are made as to how they may keep records. When children return to the computer, they will need to log on and the teacher will need to enter the teacher's password to return them to the part they left off. They can now input their results, with the computer helping to organise them. In some investigations children are asked to predict from their results. At the end they see some examples where similar investigations or patterns can be found.

The excitement and enjoyment in investigations is that they can develop in many directions. The computer deals with things in a linear way. Therefore teachers (and children) should not be restricted to the formats and directions the CD-ROM takes, rather they should try to explore as many avenues as possible. Often an investigation will trigger new questions and suggest a completely different investigation to try.

Assessing the investigations on the computer

Unfortunately artificial intelligence is not yet readily available on computers. Therefore the program assesses the children's performance according to the following simple criteria irrespective of the level they are working on:

- Not completed at all
  (Children offer no examples when returning from the practical work.)

- Partly complete
  (Children offer a few sketchy examples, many of which are incorrect.)

- Nearly complete
  (Children offer all possible examples, but have made a few errors.)

- Complete
  (Children offer all examples at that level correctly.)

The symbols used in the Progress Reports to denote these achievements are described in the section on Assessment (page 54).

The computer monitors the children's progress based on the above criteria. If they complete an investigation at their level successfully, the next time they visit the attraction they are moved up to the next level. This means that they can return to an investigation several times. They will recognise the starting point, but be offered more variety and new challenges.

For children who have regular problems with the investigations on the CD-ROM, teachers will need to work closely with them both on and off screen.

A more informative method of assessment would be for teachers to keep simple notes on the children's progress through the investigations. These can be simply based on how many examples they try, how organised they are, whether they are trying different avenues of approach and whether they are beginning to look for simple patterns and generalisations.

General description

This investigation uses the numbers found on the sides of the cable cars on the Skyride. Children focus on the digits 0 to 9 which make up the numbers, and some aspects of place value.

Equipment pack

Teachers may wish to make up the following pack in a self-sealing plastic bag, so that when children move away from the computer they have easy access to the materials they need.

- Copymaster 12
- Digit cards made from Copymaster 13
- Multilink for Level 1
- Base-10 apparatus (tens and ones for Level 2, and hundreds, tens and ones for Level 3)
- Scissors
- Pencil

At all levels children should use a mixture of digit (numeral) cards and apparatus to make the numbers within the ranges suggested. Teachers can add value to this work by asking children what would happen if:

'another 1 was added. Would it alter the tens?'

'another 10 was added. Would it alter the ones?'

and so on.

Level 1

Children are shown the numbers on the cable cars. They are then asked to identify the digits that make up a 2-digit number. These are shown as ticks on Copymaster 12. They then have to leave the computer and investigate the numbers from 1 to 20 in the same way. They can do this by using the digit cards from Copymaster 13 and by making rods of Multilink cubes. When they reach 10 it is important for teachers to show that the numbers have two parts, a ten (a rod of 10 Multilink cubes) and some ones. They record by putting a tick in the correct column on the copymaster.

The copymaster should show a pattern like this:

Name:

Skyride numbers

	1	2	3	4	5	6	7	8	9	0
1	X									
2		X								
3			X							
4				X						
5					X					
6						X				
7							X			
8								X		
9									X	
10	X									X
11	XX									
12	X	X								
13	X		X							
14	X			X						
15	X				X					
16	X					X				
17	X						X			
18	X							X		
19	X								X	
20		X								X

At this level the investigation is limited to modelling numbers, identifying digits and recording them. The children may wish to try to continue the pattern if they are beginning to become confident with higher numbers.

Level 2

Children work in a similar way to Level 1, but use the numbers in a range from 22 to 41 on copymaster 12, and report back to the computer. This range may be extended away from the machine to include numbers up to 100, and some children may wish to go further.

Most importantly, they should be encouraged to use base-10 apparatus to model the numbers as well as using digit cards.

An extension to this work could be to try to generate the patterns using numbers which grow by more than 1 at a time. For example, children could try even numbers, 50, 52, 54, 56, or odd numbers, 41, 43, 45, 47, and so on.

Whichever way children choose to grow numbers they should always be encouraged to model them with apparatus as they go along.

Different patterns will also be made by numbers which grow in threes or fives, for example:

Name:

Skyride numbers

	1	2	3	4	5	6	7	8	9	0
10	X									X
15	X				X					
20		X								X
25		X			X					
30			X							X
35			X		X					
40				X						X
45				X	X					
50					X					X
55					XX					

Level 3

This is similar to the work in Levels 1 and 2, but children investigate sets of 3-digit numbers. To report back to the computer they will use the number range from 190 to 209 on Copymaster 12. To model the numbers practically, they will need access to base-10 apparatus which includes hundreds. If they decide to extend beyond 209 they will also need another set of digit cards to make numbers like 222 and 333.

An interesting follow-up problem for children is to ask them to look at car number plates and find how many plastic nines they would need to make all the number plates from 1 to 999.

General description

This looks at combinations and permutations in terms of choices of food and drink from a menu. The screen characters, Lisa, David, Rupa and Nicky, are outside the restaurant looking for a meal. Nicky takes the children through the stages of the investigation.

Equipment pack

Teachers may wish to make up the following pack in a self-sealing plastic bag, so that when children move away from the computer they have easy access to the materials they need.

- Copymasters 3 and 4
- Pencil
- Scissors and glue
- Paper plates, cups and coloured pens for children to develop their own menus and meals, to extend the investigation and encourage further mathematical reasoning

Level 1

Children are asked to choose one drink, one meal and one sweet. To make their choices they pick up pictures of the items and put them into a chart.

They have a limited choice of drinks and sweets at this level, which restricts the number of different meals they can make. After trying the first meal on screen they are sent away to investigate any other meals they can make.

The materials provided on Copymasters 3 and 4 allow them to cut out pictures of the foods and paste them onto a chart. This work could be greatly enhanced and extended by encouraging children to draw the foods on paper plates, and the drinks on paper cups. They can then arrange these like a real meal. This will also allow them to introduce their own foods and drinks to extend the investigation later.

At Level 1 there are three different meals possible. The different combinations can be viewed as a flow chart:

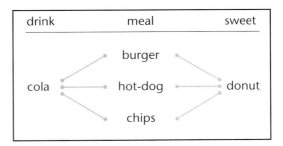

To extend the investigation at this level it is probably best to introduce a new meal each time, because this will mean just one new combination. Alternatively just one new drink or one new sweet can be added at each stage. This will introduce the work at Level 2.

Level 2

The format for Level 2 is the same as Level 1, but children have a choice of two drinks. This makes the flow chart look like this:

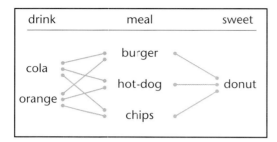

In this case there are six different combinations. Children can still try to make the combinations practically as in Level 1. However, teachers may wish to intervene at an appropriate time to suggest ways of keeping track of the combinations children have already found. It may be helpful to introduce the idea of a flow chart, but this is not essential.

To develop the work at this stage it is probably best to allow children to introduce just one new drink and investigate the changes possible. They can continue to do this until mapping the combinations becomes too difficult.

Level 3

The work follows the pattern of Levels 1 and 2, but takes away the chips and introduces another sweet. The flow chart now looks like this:

This menu now produces eight different combinations. Children can continue with the work by adding more of their own foods and finding out how this affects the number of combinations. They could add a fourth category of food like 'vegetables' or 'hot drink' and see what this does to their results.

It is probably best to restrict changes to the numbers of items to one or two categories, as the numbers of combinations can quickly become unmanageable for children at Levels 1 to 3.

The basis of a chart for further work could be as follows:

number of drinks	number of meals	number of sweets	possible combinations
1	1	1	1
1	2	1	2
1	3	1	3
	or		
1	3	1	3
2	3	1	6
3	3	1	9
	or		
1	1	1	1
2	2	1	4
3	3	1	9

General description

The Courtyard is an area of the theme park where there are side shows, games of chance and other attractions. The activity used here is a kind of Hoop-la game where children have to throw rings over the necks of the bottles. However, it is not the game that is investigated, but the way the bottles are arranged.

The investigation essentially looks at how a pattern of triangular numbers develops, but the generalisation is rather difficult for children working between Levels 1 and 3. It is more important for children to experiment with triangular arrangements and see that the rows grow in a regular way.

Equipment pack

Teachers may wish to make up the following pack in a self-sealing plastic bag, so that when children move away from the computer they have easy access to the materials they need.

- Copymaster 10 (Levels 1 and 2), Copymaster 11 (Level 3)

- Counters or adhesive spots for children to model the patterns they see on screen (or, if available, yoghurt pots or plastic bottles)

The investigation is introduced in a similar way for all three levels. Children see an arrangement of rings on bottles in a triangular formation. They are then taken step by step through the numbers of bottles in the first two rows. They develop a chart from their responses, and this is shown on screen.

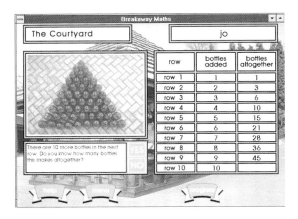

Level 1

Children are sent away from the computer to make the triangular pattern with apparatus. They will need to count the number of bottles they add for each new row, and keep a running total of the number of bottles altogether. They can record this on the top half of Copymaster 10. The number of rows should be restricted to 5, because the range of numbers at Level 1 is up to 10. Teachers may wish to mask the numbers from 6 to 10 before photocopying. This will avoid any confusion.

When children return to the computer they can put their results into a chart shown on screen.

Some children may wish to continue beyond row 5, and this would be a good way to extend the number range they are familiar with.

Level 2

The work off screen is similar to that of Level 1, but children model the triangular numbers up to the tenth row (55 bottles altogether) before they return with their results to the computer. This may take them quite a while, and they should be encouraged to keep a careful record using all of Copymaster 10.

Some children may wish to continue beyond the tenth row. Some may begin to see a pattern in the numbers on the chart and try to predict the next row as they go along. All of this should be encouraged to help them make decisions and develop mathematical reasoning.

Level 3

Children at this level cover similar ground to that in Levels 1 and 2. The work on making and monitoring decisions and developing mathematical reasoning is extended by asking them to make their own chart and keep their own results. They may use Copymaster 10 initially, but to record the results and take them back to the computer they will need to use Copymaster 11. This also introduces prediction, because they need to find the numbers of bottles in rows 15 and 20 and their totals.

Teachers can encourage children to do this by suggesting that it will take them a long time to model the triangles, and perhaps they could find a quicker way by looking at the numbers.

For Levels 1 and 2 these are the results for Copymaster 10:

Bottles		
row	bottles added	bottles altogether
row 1	1	1
row 2	2	3
row 3	3	6
row 4	4	10
row 5	5	15
row 6	6	21
row 7	7	28
row 8	8	36
row 9	9	45
row 10	10	55

For Level 3, these are the results for Copymaster 11:

Bottles		
row	bottles added	bottles altogether
row 1	1	1
row 2	2	3
row 10	10	55
row 15	15	120
row 20	20	210

Triangular numbers can be found in many situations, and children can investigate these separately. For example if sets of spots are joined to each other by lines the familiar number pattern can be generated:

spots	lines	spots and lines
2	1	
3	3	
4	6	
5	10	

The same happens when lines intersect:

lines	intersections	lines and intersections
1	0	
2	1	
3	3	
4	6	

Children can find the same pattern in staircases of squares, growing equilateral triangles and eventually in Pascal's triangle. There are also practical uses for this sequence when designing road systems and making electrical connections.

General description

The screen characters are looking at the sails on a windmill. Each sail is made from squares which make up the overall rectangular shape. Children investigate how squares can be used to make rectangles and larger squares. They will also begin to look at how these shapes grow. They may diversify into looking at using squares as a way of measuring areas.

For all levels children begin by examining a group of four small squares which make a large 2 x 2 square. On screen, they have to count the small squares and identify the big square. They are then asked how many squares there are altogether. The computer develops a chart of their results:

small squares	big squares	squares altogether
4	1	5

This chart represents Copymaster 5, which children use when they leave the computer to continue the investigation.

Equipment pack

Teachers may wish to make up the following pack in a self-sealing plastic bag, so that when children move away from the computer they have easy access to the materials they need.

- Copymasters 5, 6, 7 and 8

- Coloured pencils or crayons

- Plastic or card squares and plenty of squared paper for children to try out their own ideas and arrangements

Level 1

After the common starting exercise, children continue to investigate patterns of squares that grow by two squares at a time. This will involve the following rectangles, 2 x 3, 2 x 4 and 2 x 5. They are asked to count the number of small squares each time. They also have to identify and count the larger squares within the rectangles.

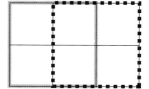

They keep records on Copymaster 5 of the total numbers of squares, which they use when they return to the computer to input their findings. Copymaster 6 provides the arrangements of squares children will need to look at. It may be used by them to outline and count small squares and big squares.

The chart develops like this

small squares	big squares	squares altogether
4	1	5
6	2	8
8	3	11
10	4	14

Children could continue the work by trying to extend the rectangle in pairs of squares. Some may begin to see the patterns of numbers in the columns (+2, +1, and +3). This is not essential at this stage.

If children use plastic or card squares to help them make the rectangles, they could explore in a different direction by trying to find other different shapes which they can make from three or four squares. They can try to give them names and record them as a display. This will be instrumental in developing ways of communicating their results, and will extend their mathematical language.

Level 2

Children continue to use small squares, but this time they look at how they can be used to make larger squares. They keep records on Copymaster 5, still counting small squares and 2 x 2 squares which can be found within the larger squares. At this level children are not expected to find 3 x 3 or 4 x 4 squares but if they do then they can be encouraged to explore these as well (see Level 3).

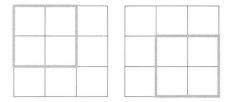

When they leave the computer to investigate further, they can use Copymaster 5 to record their results, and Copymaster 7 which has the squares they will be investigating. Their charts should have the following data to take back to the computer:

small squares	big squares	squares altogether
4	1	5
9	4	13
16	9	25
25	16	41

Children could continue the work by trying a 6 x 6 square. Some may begin to see the patterns of numbers in columns 1 and 2, which are the square numbers. They may be encouraged to predict the next number in column 3 by looking at how the numbers grow (+8, +12, +16). They may need a calculator to help with this. It is not essential to follow this up, and this should not replace any further ideas they wish to try.

Level 3

This is similar to Level 2, but asks children to find and count 1 x 1 squares, 2 x 2 squares and 3 x 3 squares in larger squares. After being shown an example on screen, they leave the computer to investigate with Copymaster 7, squared paper or plastic squares. To help record their results they can use Copymaster 8. The results they should find are represented on this chart:

1x1 squares	2x2 squares	3x3 squares	total squares
4	1	0	5
9	4	1	14
16	9	4	29
25	16	9	50

At this stage children can be encouraged to look at the patterns generated in the columns of the chart. The first three show the development of square numbers. The fourth column grows by +9, +15, +21. Children can investigate these sequences further to try to predict the results for larger squares. They can then test their predictions practically using plastic squares or squared paper.

This work is made more exciting and productive, particularly in terms of making and monitoring decisions and developing mathematical reasoning, if children work in pairs and groups. It will help them to check each other's results and predictions, and become an excellent vehicle for using mathematical language in a practical situation.

There are many other activities which can be tried with arrangements of squares. A whole range of rectangles and 'staircases' can be investigated. Children can look at irregular shapes made by squares which touch at the edges, for example:

Triominoes
'How many different shapes can you make with three squares?'

Quadrominoes
'How many different shapes can you make with four squares?'

Pentominoes
'How many different shapes can you make with five squares?'

General description

This investigation is based on the shapes found in the younger children's play area called Kiddies Kingdom. The age of children allowed to enter is restricted, therefore the characters can only view it from outside. They introduce the variety of 3D shapes which are evident in the structures of the climbing apparatus. Many of these shapes can be found in structures around the school.

Equipment pack

Teachers may wish to make up the following pack in a self-sealing plastic bag, so that when children move away from the computer they have easy access to the materials they need.

- Copymaster 9
- Examples of common 3D shapes

All Levels are introduced by looking at a cuboid. Children are shown the parts of a 3D shape and their names: 'faces', 'edges' and 'corners'.

It would be ideal for children to have a cuboid with them at the computer as they are asked to count the faces, corners and edges of the cuboid shown on the screen. As they do so, the computer develops a chart based on Copymaster 9, which is the sheet children can use to keep a record of their findings when they move away to do the practical work.

The work is differentiated by level according to the variety of shapes that children investigate.

Level 1

Children are sent away to find a pyramid. They need to count its faces, corners and edges and report their results back to the computer. A complete chart of results for all the 3D shapes is shown at the end of this section.

Level 2

Children are sent away to find a cube and a triangular prism. They need to count faces, corners and edges for both shapes before returning their results to the computer. A complete chart of results for all the 3D shapes is shown at the end of this section.

Level 3

Children are sent away to find a tetrahedron (triangular pyramid) and a hexagonal prism. They need to count faces, corners and edges for both shapes before returning their results to the computer. A complete chart of results for all the 3D shapes is shown at the end of this section.

It is essential for children to handle the real shapes each time. The set of shapes offered by the computer is limited and children may become sufficiently motivated at any level to look at a wider variety of shapes, particularly if the class set has some unusual ones.

The results for the shapes shown on the CD-ROM are shown on this chart.

name	faces	corners	edges
cuboid	6	8	12
pyramid	5	5	8
triangular prism	5	6	9
cube	6	8	12
hexagonal prism	8	12	18
tetrahedron	4	4	6

There is a relationship between the numbers of faces, edges and corners. It is known as Euler's Law, and some children may begin to 'see' it as they experiment with the shapes and make their charts. The relationship is:

faces + corners = edges + 2

This generalisation is not essential, but it may help teachers to check the results for any shapes not included here, because it applies to all shapes which have all of their surfaces flat.

Shapes with curved surfaces, like cones and cylinders may also be investigated. However, they do not follow Euler's Law in the same way.

Children will develop their mathematical language of 3D shapes and have to check and monitor their results. Counting faces, edges and corners can be difficult as it is hard to remember what you have, and haven't, counted so far. If children are encouraged to use their charts to look for relationships between faces, edges and corners they will also be developing some mathematical reasoning.

FABULOUS TOYSHOP

General description

This investigation is set in the souvenir shop at the theme park. The screen character, David, has lots of 1p and 2p coins to spend. Children have to investigate how 1p and 2p coins can be combined to make other amounts of money.

Equipment pack

Teachers may wish to make up the following pack in a self-sealing plastic bag, so that when children move away from the computer they have easy access to the materials they need:

- Copymasters 1 and 2
- Plastic (or real) 1p and 2p coins - about 10 of each
- A calculator for children who have difficulties with simple additions, and for checking work

Level 1

Children are asked to help David to make 5p using just 1p and 2p coins. The first screen they use allows them to pick up and place coins in a box until they have found 5p. The next screen shows them how the results can be written on Copymaster 1.

They are then sent away to use plastic or real coins to find all the other ways to make 5p and record their answers on Copymaster 1. Copymaster 2 can be used for children to cut and paste facsimiles of the coins onto their charts. These can be used to report back to the computer, or as a display of the work they have done. The coins could also be pasted onto

pictures of purses to show a different method of presentation.

At Level 1 there are just three solutions:

1p, 1p, 1p, 1p, 1p	**make 5p**
1p, 1p, 1p, 2p	**make 5p**
1p, 2p, 2p	**make 5p**

However, children may spend time looking at combinations which are the same, but in a different order, for example

1p, 2p, 2p; 2p, 1p, 2p; and 2p, 2p, 1p

It may take a lot of discussion before children recognise that these represent the same combination.

To develop the investigation away from the computer, children could look at other amounts, and try to find patterns.

1p	1p
2p	1p, 1p
	2p
3p	1p, 1p, 1p
	1p, 2p
4p	1p, 1p, 1p, 1p,
	1p, 1p, 2p
	2p, 2p
5p	1p, 1p, 1p, 1p, 1p
	1p, 1p, 1p, 2p
	1p, 2p, 2p
6p	1p, 1p, 1p, 1p, 1p, 1p
	1p, 1p, 1p, 1p, 2p
	1p, 1p, 2p, 2p
	2p, 2p, 2p

and so on. This may become rather difficult at this level if the amounts are extended further. However this is one way of preparing for the CD-ROM work at Level 2.

Level 2

This is similar to Level 1 and uses the same materials, but children have to find all of the combinations to make 8p. They are

1p, 1p, 1p, 1p, 1p, 1p, 1p, 1p make 8p
1p, 1p, 1p, 1p, 1p, 1p, 2p make 8p
1p, 1p, 1p, 1p, 2p, 2p make 8p
1p, 1p, 2p, 2p, 2p make 8p
2p, 2p, 2p, 2p make 8p

The same extension work as Level 1 can be used away from the computer to look at other amounts. It may also be possible to introduce the 5p coin to extend the number of possibilities, For example,

1p, 1p, 1p, 5p make 8p
1p, 2p, 5p make 8p

Level 3

This is similar to Levels 1 and 2 and uses the same materials, but children have to find all of the combinations to make 10p. They are

1p, 1p, 1p, 1p, 1p, 1p, 1p, 1p, 1p, 1p make 10p
1p, 1p, 1p, 1p, 1p, 1p, 1p, 1p, 2p make 10p
1p, 1p, 1p, 1p, 1p, 1p, 2p, 2p make 10p
1p, 1p, 1p, 1p, 2p, 2p, 2p make 10p
1p, 1p, 2p, 2p, 2p, 2p make 10p
2p, 2p, 2p, 2p, 2p make 10p

If children have not tried to make all of the other amounts to 10p, this work could be included here. The use of a 5p coin will also add to the variety of examples that children can find, and will help to develop mathematical reasoning.

Here is a chart of the combinations:

amount	number of 1p & 2p combinations	number of 1p, 2p & 5p combinations
1p	1	0
2p	2	0
3p	2	0
4p	3	0
5p	3	1
6p	4	1
7p	4	2
8p	5	2
9p	5	3
10p	6	3

Further extension work to develop mathematical reasoning can include finding the smallest number of coins needed to make a given amount. For example:

1p	1p
2p	2p
3p	1p, 2p
4p	2p, 2p
5p	5p
6p	1p, 5p
7p	2p, 5p

and so on.

ASSESSMENT AND TEACHER OPTIONS

The CD-ROM assesses children on entry to the theme park and throughout their work as they answer questions and solve problems.

The assessment on entry is simple and quick to allow children easy access to the main rides and attractions. It is only intended to give a guide to where to begin the level of questioning in the activity areas. As children move around the park the computer monitors their responses and modifies the level of difficulty according to success. At any time teachers can review children's progress through the Progress Reports in the Teacher Options Menu (see page 56).

The CD-ROM has two different ways of assessing children's success: one for activity area questions (rides) and one for investigations (attractions).

Activity area questions

For the questions based on rides, answers are either right or wrong. This allows the computer to assign a percentage for a set of 10 questions and it decides whether to set further questions at a higher or lower stage according to the following criteria:

Children score 90% to 100% correct

The next time children visit this subject area (for example Number 2), on whatever ride, they are given questions from the next stage upwards.

Children score 70% to 89% correct

Children have to achieve this score twice on the same subject area (for example, Number 2) before they move up a stage. This has to be on the two rides that are dedicated to that subject area.

Children score 50% to 69% correct

Children must do the set of questions on the other ride dedicated to the same subject area (for example Number 2). If they score the same they must repeat either or both question sets until they score 70% to 89% on both, or 90% to 100% on one.

Children score less than 50% correct

If they score this on both question sets on the rides dedicated to this subject area (for example Number 2) then they are moved down a stage to allow them to regain success. If they score less than 50% on one ride and above 50% on the other, then the above criteria are used to evaluate their performance.

Investigations (attractions)

A different method of assessment is used for the six investigations to be found at the attractions. This takes into account more of the Using and Applying Mathematics thread in the National Curriculum.

- Not completed at all: 0% response (Children offer no examples when returning from the practical work).

- Partly complete: less than 60% correct (Children offer a few sketchy examples, many of which are incorrect).

- Nearly complete: 60% to 99% complete (Children offer all possible examples, but have made a few errors).

■ Complete: 100% complete
(Children offer all examples at that
level correctly).

Children who complete an
investigation will visit it at the next
level when they return to the
attraction. If children do not complete
an investigation they get another
chance to try it at the same level the
next time they arrive at the attraction.

There is a simple chart in the
Progress Report section of the Teacher
Options menu (see page 57) for
teachers to see how successful children
have been. Teachers may wish to use
this to decide when to intervene in an
investigation and offer suggestions.

Note: In order for pupil's scores to
be updated when they have completed
an investigation/activity area, they
must pass through the exit screen of
that area.

The CD-ROM is designed to allow children to explore the theme park freely and solve problems along the way. To allow teachers to take some control of the work, the Teacher Options menu offers eight functions. Teachers need to use their personal teacher's password to access the menu. (see p58)

1 Progress report on pupils

This provides two kinds of histogram: one for the rides, which contain the activity area questions; and another for the attractions, which contain the investigations.

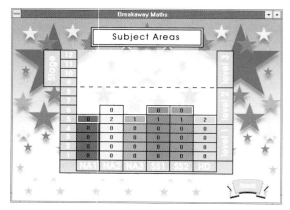

The rides

Using their password (see p58) teachers can access a progress report histogram for each child or group of children. The histogram has the following codes along the horizontal axis:

NA1 NA2 NA3 SS1 SS2 HD

NA stands for Number and Algebra, SS stands for Shape, Space and Measures, HD stands for Handling Data.

The right-hand side of the histogram shows the three levels at Key Stage 1. The left-hand side shows the four stages into which each level has been divided to structure the CD-ROM:

Stages 1 to 4	Level 1
Stages 5 to 8	Level 2
Stages 9 to 12	Level 3

The histogram shows the name of the group and a set of bars showing the stages at which they are currently working in each area of mathematics. A figure in a box indicates the number of fresh attempts the pupil made at that particular subject level. This allows teachers to see where children are strong or weak, and allows for differentiation within the maths curriculum. For example, children may be successful in Handling Data (HD/Number 5ab), but less so with place value (NA1/Number 2abc). Teachers can use this information to modify any Individual Education Plans for children.

WARNING. The computer is not infallible. Nothing replaces teacher observation and assessment.

There is a blank facsimile of the screen histogram on Copymaster 14 so that teachers can make a quick record of the results they see on the screen.

It is not envisaged that this function would be used after each session. Teachers may wish to review progress on a weekly, monthly, or half-termly basis.

The attractions

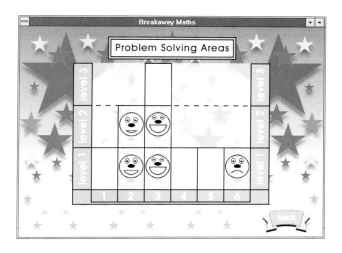

The progress report histogram allows teachers to find out how successful each group of children has been in the investigations.

The horizontal axis has the numbers of the investigations. These are:

1   Skyride ....Digits and place value

2   Explorer Restaurant ..Food combinations

3   Courtyard ....Triangular numbers

4   Old MacDonald's Farm ....Squares

5   Kiddies Kingdom ....3D shapes

6   Fabulous Toyshop ....Coin combinations

To indicate whether children have tried the investigation faces appear in the columns. The level that the face is on indicates the National Curriculum Level of the investigation attempted. This can be read off the vertical axis.

The expression on the face indicates the degree of success:

- A sad face means the investigation was not attempted (children quitted and moved on without attempting the problems).

- A neutral face means that the investigation was attempted, but with little success (less than 60% of the responses were correct).

- A smiling face means that the children had some success with the investigation and completed it at that level, but did not score 100%.

- A laughing face means that the children completed the investigation completely at that level and will move on to the next level when they return.

To help teachers keep a record of children's achievements, Copymaster 15 provides a blank histogram for teachers to copy the faces or make their own notes on children's progress.

It is not envisaged that this function would be used after each session. Investigations will quite often become long-term projects and may take more time than the assessment questions. Teachers may wish to review progress on a monthly, or half-termly basis.

Information from both types of progress report can be used by teachers to make decisions on the use of the other functions on the Teacher Options Menu.

2 Set the level of the questions

This function is only available when children are logged on. If teachers select this function and type in the filename of a particular group, or individual, they can override the computer's decisions about which levels of question children can access on rides and attractions.

This is useful if teachers feel that a child or group is working at too high or too low a level. It may be desirable to keep children at a particular level to help them gain confidence or allow them to be successful. Alternatively, teachers may want to sit with an individual child and use the questions at a higher level as part of an assessment procedure.

To change the difficulty of questions on rides, teachers need to input the *stage* they wish to set. Remember:

Level 1 is stages 1 to 4

Level 2 is stages 5 to 8

Level 3 is stages 9 to 12

Attractions, which contain the investigations, are organised in National Curriculum *levels* of difficulty and teachers can set them at Level 1, Level 2 or Level 3. This function may be best used to extend an investigation where children are working enthusiastically and well. For example, they may do very well on triangular numbers at Level 1, and want to try some more. Teachers can set up Level 2 for them so that they can continue

as far as they wish.

To cancel any changes you have made and return to the original levels, click on the restore button.

3 Go to a ride or an attraction

4 Go to a subject

These perform similar functions. Teachers can go to a ride and find out which part of the National Curriculum Programme of Study it covers. They can do the same for attractions and find information about the investigations they use.

Similarly teachers can go to a subject area (Programme of Study) and find which rides offer questions to cover it. This is a useful way for teachers to become familiar with the layout and content of the theme park. It can also be used in conjunction with '2 Set the level of questions' to help with assessment.

The rest of the Teacher Options are to do with management of the CD-ROM.

5 Change password

On delivery, the password protecting the Teacher Options Menu is set to the word DEFAULT. If children discover this password, they can use all of the above options. This could cause some degree of chaos. Therefore teachers are advised to input a new password to keep the Teacher Options menu safe. Colleagues should be advised of this and any subsequent changes of teacher password.

6 Select pupil directory

This allows teachers to change the directory where the pupils' progress records are stored. This allows you to use a different directory for each class. The current directories and files are displayed. Having created directories to which records will subsequently be saved you use this option to select the directory you wish to view or save to. This option is only available if nobody is logged on to the disc.

7 Tutorial overview

This provides a summary of the main features of the CD-ROM.

8 Delete pupil's files

If a pupil's file is no longer needed it can be deleted using this facility from time to time in order to get rid of unwanted files thereby freeing disc space.

9 Delete audio

The Teacher Options menu screen has a loudspeaker icon in the top left hand corner. Click on this to turn off the audio on the disc. It should be noted that the audio has been provided to allow access to the mathematics for children with reading difficulties. Before the audio is turned off you will be prompted by the computer to establish whether you want to remove this facility.

COPYMASTERS

Name:

Coins to make ... ☐

coins	total

Copymaster 1

Name:

Coins to cut and paste

Cut   Cut   Cut   Cut   Cut

1p	1p	1p	1p
1p	1p	1p	1p
1p	1p	1p	1p
1p	1p	1p	1p
2p	2p	2p	2p
2p	2p	2p	2p

Cut   Cut   Cut   Cut   Cut

Copymaster 2

Breakaway MATHS CD-Rom   © Peter and Jenny Gash 1995 • Published by Thomas Nelson and Sons Ltd

Name:

Menu chart

drink	meal	sweet

Copymaster 3

Name:

Food to cut and paste

Cut   **Cut**   **Cut**   **Cut**   **Cut**   **Cut**

Cut

| cola | cola | cola | cola | cola |

Cut

| orange | orange | orange | orange | orange |

Cut

| hot dog | hot dog | hot dog | hot dog | hot dog |

Cut

| burger | burger | burger | burger | burger |

Cut

| chips | chips | chips | chips | chips |

Cut

| donut | donut | donut | donut | donut |

Cut

| ice cream | ice cream | ice cream | ice cream | ice cream |

Cut

Copymaster 4

Breakaway
MATHS
CD-Rom
© Peter and Jenny Gash 1995 • Published by Thomas Nelson and Sons Ltd

Name:

Squares

small squares	big squares	squares altogether

Copymaster 5

Squares on the windmill

Copymaster 6

© Peter and Jenny Gash 1995 • Published by Thomas Nelson and Sons Ltd

Name:

Squares

Copymaster 7

 *Breakaway MATHS CD-Rom* © Peter and Jenny Gash 1995 • Published by Thomas Nelson and Sons Ltd

Name:

Squares inside squares

small squares	big squares	very big squares	squares altogether

Copymaster 8

Breakaway
MATHS
CD-Rom
© Peter and Jenny Gash 1995 • Published by Thomas Nelson and Sons Ltd

| Name: | | | |

Solid shapes

name	faces	corners	edges
cuboid			

Copymaster 9

Name:

Bottles

row	bottles added	bottles altogether
row 1		
row 2		
row 3		
row 4		
row 5		
row 6		
row 7		
row 8		
row 9		
row 10		

Copymaster 10

Bottles

row	bottles added	bottles altogether
row 1		
row 2		
row 10		
row 15		
row 20		

Copymaster 11

Breakaway
MATHS
CD-Rom   © Peter and Jenny Gash 1995 • Published by Thomas Nelson and Sons Ltd

Name:

Skyride numbers

	1	2	3	4	5	6	7	8	9	0

Copymaster 12

Name:

Digit cards to cut out

Cut · Cut · Cut · Cut · Cut · Cut

1	2	3	4	5

Cut

6	7	8	9	0

Cut

1	2	3	4	5

Cut

6	7	8	9	0

Cut

1	2	3	4	5

Cut

6	7	8	9	0

Cut

Copymaster 13

Breakaway MATHS CD-Rom © Peter and Jenny Gash 1995 • Published by Thomas Nelson and Sons Ltd

Name:

Progress Chart

Subject Areas

	NA1	NA2	NA3	SS1	SS2	HD	
12							Level 3
11							Level 3
10							Level 3
9							Level 3
8							Level 2
7							Level 2
6							Level 2
5							Level 2
4							Level 1
3							Level 1
2							Level 1
1							Level 1
	NA1	NA2	NA3	SS1	SS2	HD	

Copymaster 14

Name:

Investigation Progress Chart

Investigation	Level 1	Level 2	Level 3
1. Digits in Numbers (Skyride)			
2. Food Combinations (Explorer			
3. Triangular Numbers (Courtyard)			
4. Squares (Old MacDonald's			
5. 3-D Shapes (Kiddies			
6. Coin Combinations (Fabulous Toyshop)			

Copymaster 15

Breakaway MATHS CD–Rom   © Peter and Jenny Gash 1995 • Published by Thomas Nelson and Sons Ltd

About Granada Learning

On January 1st 1998 YITM became part of the Granada Media Group. This already successful partnership, which became the complete solution provider in education, will continue to offer a wide range of innovative and high quality CD-Roms and software under the new name of Granada Learning.

Granada Learning is a mail order company with order fulfilment within 14 days of order receipt. The overseas section of the company is organised using approved agencies and distributors.

There is an excellent technical helpline available should customers experience any problems using Granada Learning products.

To keep customers informed of new products, training opportunitities and special promotions the company attends UK and international exhibitions and organises presentations and training.

Three annual catalogues are produced (primary, secondary and special needs) for launch in September with supplements of additional information being offered throughout the year.

If you would like any further information about our range of software titles please contact us at;

Granada Learning Ltd.

Granada Television

Quay Street

Manchester

M60 9EA

Tel : 0161 827 2927

Fax : 0161 827 2966

Email : info@granada-learning.com

Website : www.granada-learning.com

Science series

■ ELEMENTS   *Age group: 14–16 yrs*

Versions: Acorn, PC and Mac

The 1993 European Multimedia Award winning CD-ROM that enables you to learn about the 104 Materials in the Periodic Table and about Atomic structure in exciting, innovative and effective ways.

■ MATERIALS   *Age group: 12–16 yrs*

Versions: Acorn, PC and Mac

A fully interactive journey around the world of science that enables you to carry out real experiments on screen. Explore the properties and characteristics of over 150 materials and test your skills on a truly educational game that will help you learn as you play.

■ ELECTRICITY AND MAGNETISM (Primary Edition)
Age group: 10–11 yrs

■ ELECTRICITY AND MAGNETISM (Secondary Edition)
Age group: 11–13 yrs

Versions: Acorn and PC

The content of the disc relates to electricity in the home, power generation and scientific theory. It uses animation, video, photographs and text to explain and to bring the subject matter to life. A comprehensive range of electronic tools is available to pupils to help them find their way around the disc, locate and handle information.

■ WATER   *Age group: 11–16 yrs*

Versions: Acorn and PC

Explore every aspect of water in the environment. Investigate its use in the home, industry and for transport, recreation and fishing. Seventeen in-depth case studies investigate major environmental issues on a world stage.

■ LAND AND AIR   *Age group: 11–16 yrs*

Versions: Acorn and PC

Investigates six major environmental issues including natural disasters, dwindling resources, conservation, food & famine, air quality and changing climate. Specially commissioned video sequences provide introductions to each issue which can then be examined in depth using powerful navigational tools.

Introduction to the Environment Series

Three packages that introduce environmental issues on separate CD-ROMs.

■ CONSERVATION   *Age group: 10–16 yrs*

Versions: Acorn and PC

Case studies of world famous national parks which are used to illustrate the benefits and difficulties of conserving wilderness, wild areas and threatened species.

■ CHANGING CLIMATE   *Age group: 11–16 yrs*

Versions: Acorn and PC

Explores the facts and theories of global warming and climate change.

■ DWINDLING RESOURCES
Age group: 10–16 yrs

Versions: Acorn and PC

Examine the ways in which the key natural resources of water, forest, oil and coal have been used over the last two hundred years to sustain and support lifestyles, and the effect this has had on the environment.

Humanities series

■ JOURNEYS INTO HISTORY
Age group: 9–13 yrs

Versions: Acorn and PC

The journeys in question take pupils to case studies on the Romans (at Hadrian's wall), early Christianity (on Lindisfarne), life in Medieval times including the building of the great cathedrals (based on Durham) and the development of the first railways (Stockton). Each relates to wider aspects of British history and to other locations throughout Britain. Each provides a rich opportunity to study historical topics in a fresh and exciting way using multimedia.

■ HOW WE USED TO LIVE: EARLY VICTORIANS *Age group: 7–11 yrs*

■ HOW WE USED TO LIVE: LATE VICTORIANS *Age group: 11–14 yrs*

Versions: Acorn and PC

Based on the highly successful television series, these discs facilitate in-depth historical studies of the period. Using dramatic clips as starting points to significant investigations, the discs provide a rich source of historical material accompanied with easy to use information retrieval and manipulation tools.

■ WORLD WAR II – GLOBAL CONFLICT *Age group: 14–16 yrs*

Versions: Acorn and PC

Winner of the European Multimedia Award 1994/5 for the best educational CD-ROM title. Produced in collaboration with the US National Archive, this disc provides an exciting and accessible introduction to the events, themes and personalities of the Second World War. Five interactive video sequences provide a chronological introduction from which investigations in depth can be made using powerful search, retrieval and information handling tools.

■ WORLD WAR II – SOURCES AND ANALYSIS *GCSE/A Level*

Versions: Acorn and PC

Uses original materials from the US National Archive to bring you the significant events of World War II as viewed not only by those who fought but also by those who lived and worked on the Home Front. The disc is divided into themes, case studies and source materials.

■ RELIGIONS OF THE WORLD
Age group: 11–16 yrs

Versions: Acorn and PC

Eight major world religions can be investigated under the headings of beliefs, forms of worship, scriptures, artefacts, festivals, people, religious communities and places of worship. A separate section applies information from other parts of the disc to consider major contemporary issues.

- **THE PHYSICAL WORLD**
  Age group: 11–16 yrs

Versions: Acorn and PC

An exploration of the physical features of the planet and the processes that formed them. Case studies in the Natural Hazards section describe the causes and consequences of some of the most dramatic events of the natural world. The People and their Environment section examines the interaction between people and different environments.

Languages series

- **EN ROUTE**
  Age group: 10+ beginners

Versions: Acorn and PC

A fully interactive multimedia CD-ROM for the student starting to learn French. It will involve you in a stimulating learning experience that uses multimedia to its full potential. Three levels of difficulty are available to help you learn at your own pace. Vocabulary and grammar support are available to assist with the hundreds of interactive exercises that will immerse you in the language. You can also record your own pronunciation and compare it with that of native speakers.

- **¡EN MARCHA!** (Intermediate Spanish) *Age group: 14–16 yrs*

and

- **DIRECTIONS 2000** (Intermediate French) *Age group: 14–16 yrs*

Versions: Acorn and PC

Each of these discs contains over two hours of spoken language illustrated with a vast library of coloured images and graphics. The discs support the development of vocabulary and provide facilities for you to practise pronunciation. Both discs contain language learning games.

Early reading series

- **MAX AND THE MACHINES**
  Age range: 4–7 yrs

- **MAXIMANIA** *Age range: 4-7 yrs*

Versions: Acorn and PC

CD-ROMs that support the development of essential reading skills such as sorting, sequencing, matching and, in the case of Maximania, comprehension. They draw on the successful Flying Boot reading scheme by Professor Ted Wragg, illustrated by Val Biro and published by Thomas Nelson. Both discs are packed with material that will captivate and motivate young children. On-screen activities make these 'Active Learning' discs.

For further information about these and future titles contact:

Granada Learning, Granada Television, Quay Street, Manchester, M60 9EA.